# Munch Munch

Written by Lisa Thompson
Pictures by Craig Smith

"I am hungry,"
said the starfish.

Munch, munch.

3

A little fish came along.

Munch, munch.

"Yum! That was good," it said.

Along came a big fish.

"That little fish looks good," it said.

Munch, munch.

Then a big shark came along.

"I am very hungry," it said.

Munch, munch.

"Ouch!" said the shark.

A hook was stuck in its teeth.

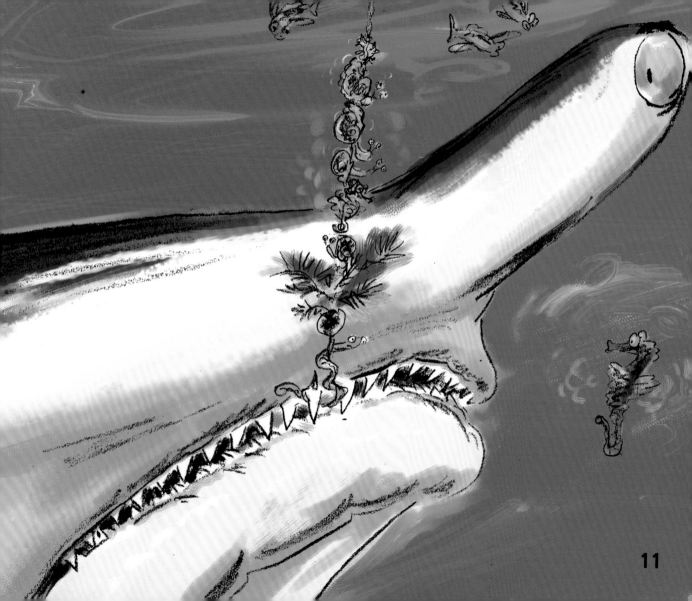

"I have a fish!"
said the Captain.
"Fish for lunch."

"Oh no!" said the Captain.

"That fish is too big.

I am not very hungry now!"